While We Waited

Written by: Jeffrey Miller-McGrail, M.ED
Illustrated by: Meaghan Moore

Author's Dedication

To Brandyn, my partner-in-waiting. I love you more than I could ever express in words.

To our baby, we may still be waiting for you, but we love you so much..

To our baby's birth family, thank you will never be enough.

To everyone who has supported us on our journey...this one's for you.

Illustrator's Dedication

I'd like to thank my amazing family and my friends for supporting my artistic endeavors, especially my wonderful mother.

I'd also like to thank Jeff for reaching out and sharing this amazing experience with me.

I loved working on this book, and I hope whoever reads this enjoys it just as much.

Pictured above is the Adoption Triad. It represents the child, the birth parents, the adoptive parents, and the bonds created between them all during the adoption process.

Author's Note

Adoption is the act of choosing. When my husband and I de-cided to grow our family, we knew that adoption was the path for us. We chose to open our hearts to the many joys, and pains, that come along with the adoption process. We chose to open our hearts to the wait...to the love...to the adoption triad of birth family, adoptive family, and child.

For anyone who has chosen this journey, you know that it in-cludes many steps and can take many years. This is the story of our wait...a story that I hope will inspire you to grow and evolve during your own wait. A wait that looks different for everyone.

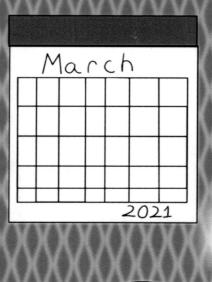

A journey begins!

...and we biked.

...and we cooked.

...and we made memories.

...and we grew.

About the Author

Jeffrey Miller-McGrail is a husband, educator, dog and cat dad, son, uncle, and hopeful adoptive parent. He lives in New Jersey with his husband.

Jeffrey, along with his husband, operates the social media for Jacob H+, a personal community of support for those waiting to be placed with a baby for adoption. Find us on Instagram @jacobhplus and Facebook at Jacob H+.

About the Illustrator

Meaghan Moore is a graduate of Georgian Court University, currently residing in New Jersey with her family.

She gained a love for art in high school, and later a specific interest in illustration during college. She plans to illustrate as a career. You can find her on indeed.com!

Made in United States
North Haven, CT
01 November 2022

26198633R00015